*Born in a Stable*

Dorothy Calcutt

John, aged about 60, sitting on the wall outside his home in Freeland with his friend Tom Edginton.

# Born in a Stable

DOROTHY CALCUTT

A companion to
*The Salt of the Earth*

THE WYCHWOOD PRESS

Our books may be ordered from bookshops or (post free) from
Jon Carpenter Publishing, Alder House, Market Street, Charlbury, OX7 3PH

wychwood@joncarpenter.co.uk

Please send for our free Wychwood Press catalogue

Credit card orders should be phoned or faxed to 01689 870437
or 01608 811969

First published in 2001 by
Jon Carpenter Publishing
Alder House, Market Street, Charlbury, Oxfordshire OX7 3PH
☎ 01608 811969

ISBN  1 902279 13 1

Printed in England by J. W. Arrowsmith Ltd., Bristol

# Contents

# Acknowledgements

Many thanks to the following who have been kind enough to help me with this book.

Mrs Mason who allowed access to the stable block at Bowles Farm.

Jon Carpenter for photography at the farm and the grave.

Brian Hodgson for political correctness.

Lyne Munro and David Newburn, and Alex, who have recently bought and occupy the Freeland home.

Richard Bidgood for information about the glove factories.

John Stonebridge for details of the stag hunting season.

Doreen Stroud (Druce) for identifying Tom Edginton.

Tony Benn for conventional heritage procedure.

The Welland and Deeping Internal Drainage Board for photographs.

Gerald Gracey-Cox for research.

Trevor Tyrrell for local help in the Fens.

My own family, Godfrey, Madge, Bridget and Colin, for transport and photography.

My son-in-law, Richard Owen, for all the computer work.

# Preface

'More, more, more' was the response that echoed back to me after *The Salt of the Earth* was published. I was always sorry I hadn't started the saga at a point fifty years earlier, so in this book I am attempting to correct this omission.

My mother, who had whispered it to me, knew the wealthy family from the north that is described here. I have no reason to disbelieve her as I have verified all her other statements.

I will say this much, that the male concerned was an earl, but later forfeited his earldom. On consulting *Burke's Peerage* I found two earls fitting this description. Even after a lapse of one hundred and fifty years, I think this stone is best left unturned, so all names have been changed.

In view of this, the events concerning this family are mostly fiction, but they are loosely based on a different family, faced with a similar situation. All the happenings in Oxfordshire are factual.

The Three Horseshoes, recently modernised, still stands in Long Hanborough. This coaching inn was situated on the A4095, at that time the main road from London to Gloucester. The A40 was built to the south between 1930 and 1940.

I never knew either my grandmother (Georgina) or my great grand-mother (Emma). Georgina died in 1901 but Emma outlived her by several years.

John, the main character, lived in his Freeland home until his death in 1940.

# — 1 —

# Expectations

Henry trudged up the moors. A cold east wind was sweeping across, but he hardly noticed it. He had reason to feel inwardly happy – he was well fed and clothed in Harris tweeds, he had plenty of money in the bank, a full hip flask in his pocket, and he had a large estate to use until the end of his days. He was healthy and strong; he loved the bracing air and the loneliness that nature afforded to his own landscape. Today, however, this was as nothing compared to the news that his wife had given him earlier in the day. They already had one three-year-old son but he was born a weakling and recently they had put him in a home, knowing full well that he would not live much longer.

This news however would alter everything; he knew that in his bones. The expected son would be strong. He personally would determine his upbringing; no pampering for the next one.

His wife was proving to be rather reluctant to mother a large family. He – in his innocence – thought that all females found families rewarding. He would not consider letting down his ancestors.

So, with a spring in his step, he reached the summit of his lands. He loved this spot; the limestone outcrop formed a path, fissured by unmeasured, giraffe-like lines. From these cracks emerged many flowers, wild pansies and grasses, sometimes thrift or cheddar pinks. How the seed got there or how long ago one would never know, but they had survived and overcome all difficulties that this untilled virgin land had offered them.

The real attraction of this spot was the fact that he could turn around through three hundred and sixty degrees and each panoramic view was all his. 'This is all mine,' he would think aloud, 'and now there is every hope that I will be passing it on to the next generation.' As he stood there, deep in thought, he could pick out the hamlet over which he had complete control. Just one formidable, unyielding, battlemented stronghold, resembling a cold castle more than the intimacy of a warm home. The adjacent church, built in a similar mode, demanded obedience from the local inhabitants of the few poverty-stricken cottages. He could even see the thin curls of smoke rising from their chimneys, curling towards the west as usual.

His mind was active. Boys' names, a baby's needs, nurses and tutors. Then he got down to fundamentals; yes, he must start today. His wife should take a walk each day – he was sure he could supervise that. Rest and exercise, that was the recipe for a strong baby. No more tapestry work for her.

He felt pride and satisfaction as he descended those moors. This son is *his*, his wife merely a warm, controlled environment in which *his* son would grow and develop. He would be born with a silver spoon in his mouth, both literally and proverbially.

So it was on this momentous day that a rigid ritual was put in motion. He walked around the large, walled garden with Moira every day; then, when she was sitting on the chesterfield, he lifted her feet and covered them with a fur rug. That was the nearest he ever came to endearments. Then and only then he would retire to his own room and enjoy a cigar in peace and solitude. No smoke must ever get near his wife now.

Walking in the kitchen garden had a second benefit. They could give instructions to the gardener, demanding the exact vegetables and fruit that the household required. While the gardener cultivated the soil, they cultivated an interest in growing, harvesting, cooking and even eating the produce.

The gardener did not appreciate this new routine. He could no longer take his rest in the potting shed. He was obliged to show restraint and tolerance. His own house, employment and family depended on him keeping his job.

The staff had not yet been given the family news, but they knew all right, in fact everyone in the hamlet knew. They had all mourned with their employers when the health of the first-born deteriorated. The prospect was rosier now, but they well knew that doctors, nurses and many more would increase their work.

During the following months both Henry and Moira supervised the renovation of the nursery. They persevered with their walks – in fact Moira began to anticipate them with pleasure. Henry bought a Paisley shawl to keep Moira's shoulders warm in bed.

He occasionally found sufficient time to stride up to his haunt at the viewpoint. The excursion took at least two hours but it provided him with thinking time. The name of his son was mulled over and over and, because he knew in his heart that he would be healthy, hardy and strong, he secretly chose the name Leo. This was his decision, never discussed with anyone.

The gardener was still obeying his instructions; the leeks were monsters this year, the asparagus, the artichokes and potatoes had all exceeded expectations. Henry had forgone his grouse shoot this season but he had enjoyed an occasional foxhunt. The winter had not been too severe although there had been one or two falls of snow, which the bleak wind had whipped into drifts.

With the comfort of her new moleskin coat Moira had persevered with her walks so her lungs were filled with fresh, clear air once a day.

The older son had passed away; this unmentionable topic had been lifted from their hearts as a cloud passes silently across the sun. The whole household was becoming irritated and impatient with waiting. Then at ten o'clock one night late in March the procedure was set in motion. One nurse had been installed earlier but another was quickly fetched, as was the doctor. Fires were banked with fuel throughout the mansion. All servants were kept up, and wet nurses were notified of the impending event.

This situation lasted for forty-eight hours. A nurse assured Henry that all was well but very slow. The household took turns in sleeping and feeding the extra mouths. Henry was subdued and nervous but he did send to the gardener for a bouquet of flowers. Then – in the middle of the night – the baby's lungs could clearly be heard. Henry's first question was, 'How heavy is he?'

The doctor had a quiet talk with Henry. 'You have an eight-pound son,' he announced. 'Your wife has had a very worrying time, because the infant was too big for her bone size. I think she will recover with rest, but I guarantee she will never be able to give birth again.'

Henry dismissed the statement but he had recorded it in his mind.

Two wet nurses were installed, one for the day and one for the night. Moira should take no responsibility; this suited Henry, as he wanted no bond to develop between mother and son.

So it was that Leo started his life, already mapped out for him, as a confident, robust and outgoing individual.

# — 2 —

# Male chauvinism

All Henry's drafted schemes were now launched. No architect had ever masterminded such a detailed procedure for the progress and development of one solitary infant who was oblivious to all the rules and regulations surrounding him. These orders were written and posted for all to see.

The doctor would stay until Moira was allowed out of bed. Two nurses would stay for about a fortnight, then just one indefinitely. The two wet nurses were already taking up their duties. More work was piled on to the cook and maids; the gardener was more involved too.

The babe was actually no worry at all. He was weighed daily, he was monitored in every way. He was not a beautiful baby, long limbs, wide shoulders, and a huge head. He was however very strong; that pleased his father and to him alone he was very, very beautiful.

He was to have nothing but breast milk until he was nine months old. Then Henry dictated his diet. Beef broth most days made only with beef from Aberdeen Angus steers. He could ring the changes with knuckle of veal. Leo was now crawling and took his first steps on his first birthday.

The three of them, Henry, Moira and Leo, walked slowly around the garden. Moira never lifted the boy, she was considered too weak. That suited Henry; keep the female away from the male.

The year soon passed away and at two years his father reasoned that he was capable of walking with him. So they set off together to the viewpoint. The little legs persevered right to the top. Although it was doubtful if his young brain could comprehend, for the first time in his young life he was told, 'All this is mine, and one day it will all be yours.'

Henry had two golden retrievers and one English springer. Leo loved them so much that his father bought and gave him a golden retriever pup, Goldie; it was kept in a kennel just outside his window. They soon became great friends; they were inseparable. The last nurse had been exchanged for a nanny. She had received her rules. 'You are to teach him to do everything for himself – no spoon feeding – only independence and self confidence.'

On his third birthday he could not be found. Panic set in. The nanny asked the gardener; no luck there; she asked the groom; no luck there either. She called Leo; she called Goldie. She delayed telling the master and missus; she dreaded the expected frustration, the anger and tempers. When at last Henry was informed, he calmly said, 'I'll find him, I know where he is.'

So, alone, Henry strode with purpose to the viewpoint – yes – there he was concentrating on the pavement not daring to step on the cracks. Goldie was keeping the whole situation under control.

Leo received no grumbles or indeed praise for this episode, Henry showed no reaction. He indeed viewed it as his first reward for his method of rearing an independent, healthy, robust son.

Leo stood up straight. 'All this will be mine,' he proudly told his father. This was music to Henry's ears; he was secretly patting himself on the back. This incident welded father and son together; they understood each other perfectly.

At the age of four, Leo was considered competent for a standard education. Henry travelled by carriage and pair with Leo's newly appointed tutor to the nearby town. Together they chose a library for the lad. It included Shakespeare, odes by John Keats, poems by Wordsworth, and essays by Charles Lamb. They added a dictionary and a beginner's book called *Highway to English Literature*. Quite a catalogue for a four-year-old but he was already well read with the Bible. Leo was anxious, willing and able.

His study hours should be from nine-thirty to twelve noon. Henry and Leo would then enjoy a walk across the moors before returning for their midday meal. The rest of the day would be spent in acquainting the child with natural and scientific knowledge, the soil, the plants, the birds and trees and how they were all interdependent. At the end of the day the tutor would read a chosen passage from a book or Leo's favourite poem. Sleeping was never a problem; he had uncontrollable energy, an enormous appetite, plenty of clean fresh air, all ingredients of sound sleep.

The older he grew the more his son's schooling increased but still Henry loved those afternoons explaining the more important things in life. How to shake hands correctly, how to hold and direct a conversation, how to treat members of staff and snub them if the need arose; the meaning of words like aristocracy, nobles, peerage, lords, etc.

Then to the necessary qualifications for the ideal wife. First is the birth and rank but coupled with this is physical strength. 'This is where I made my mistake,' he told his son. 'Your mother is too weak to have a bigger family.' He was resigned to the fact now, although he shrugged off the message and had barely registered it when the doctor originally told him.

Now he emphasised the point to his son again. 'You are the only one to carry on the family name, the only one who can legitimately stand on the viewpoint and say, "This will be all mine". Yes, your partner must be tall, strong and have large hips, but the breeding must be unquestionable.

'Scrutinise each likely female – then give them an undisclosed challenge, walk them on the moors, take them to the viewpoint. If they cannot keep up the pace, if they grumble or stumble, just cross them from your list. Remember this is no love match, it has more to do with durability than compatibility. There are lots of eligible girls but only one Leo.

'I myself searched the orchard then chose the sweetest, prettiest apple. I expect you to choose very carefully the largest, dual purpose apple with excellent keeping qualities, growing on a tree with the correct rootstock.'

# — 3 —

# Leo chooses

On Sundays the family attended matins. They sat in the front pew, but even from that spot they discreetly viewed the congregation, making sure that every member of the community was there. As they left the church they shook hands with each parishioner in their correct pecking order.

This particular Sunday the head gardener's seventeen-year-old daughter failed to appear. Henry said to the trainee gardener, 'I didn't see Sarah today, is she not well?'

'Oh,' was the reply, 'a girl in her condition tries not to be seen.'

Henry had not heard or even guessed that she was expecting a baby; he wouldn't have such behaviour on his estate. If this were correct, she would have to go. He reflected on the situation; no, he would not accept such behaviour. He called on the head gardener and asked about the gossip.

'I'm afraid it is true, sir,' he replied. 'She will not name the father.'

'I do not have such babies here so she must find somewhere else to live.'

'You are actually turning her out of her home, is that your decision?' the workman asked.

'That is my decision. I don't want to discuss it further.'

'In that case sir,' he replied, 'the whole family will move house and employment. I do not like the situation either, but I will not, indeed I could not, leave my daughter in the lurch.'

'Think it over tonight,' Henry concluded. 'Let me know tomorrow if you change your mind; it is unwise to make a snap decision.'

Henry did not want to lose his capable gardener. This situation was not foreseen. His standards were not there to be challenged.

During the night the gardener, his wife, his daughter and one younger son tied up what clothes they had in a bundle. Taking as much food as they had, they left the hamlet and trudged down by the little stream out of Henry's domain and into the small town.

They knew of a mill where they were hoping to get work. Luckily there was one empty tied cottage, for any family that had at least two members to work in the factory. Out of their despair came hope of a new life.

Back at the hamlet Henry was expecting a change of heart from his workman, instead of which he had lost a competent man. He had no option now; he called in the trainee and promoted him, never guessing that he was indeed the guilty one.

Henry seized the opportunity to emphasise to his son what was likely to happen to pretty girls. Goldie had recently died but Leo knew that a dog is only a pet so he wouldn't grieve. He had wanted a horse, but after discussing the suggestion with his father, together they decided the possibility of an accident was too great.

'If you had brothers, I would welcome it, but should anything befall you now, I would blame myself.' Henry sold his own horse immediately.

Leo was coming to his eighteenth birthday and was often crossing the moors with his gun; at least he could share that pleasure with his father.

Meanwhile Henry was already listing all possible girls with the correct wealth and station.

Then at last, Henry collected the first female in his carriage. His footman accompanied them. She was to stay for one night. They dined together, but in the morning Leo did not even take her to the moors, her moaning and complaining of tiredness irritated him. She had been travelling all day but he dismissed that fact. When she mounted the carriage the following day Leo handed her a parcel which contained a pair of gloves. This was a prearranged method of telling his father he did not wish to see her again. Henry would then know how to converse on the return journey. Leo's mother had warmed to the girl.

The next applicant – that was how Leo viewed them – had arrived with flimsy clothes and shoes, so she was given the cold shoulder with her parcel of gloves. The following day Leo's gold cuff links were missing, he searched vainly, but Henry dismissed the suggestion that she had taken them. 'Just those idle, pilfering servants, I'll buy you some monogrammed ones to replace them.'

The next one could talk of nothing but samplers and stitching – she received the same leaving present. The next improved a little, she walked the moors, but tended to drag behind so no way would he take her to the viewpoint. Another pair of gloves went there.

Gloves disappeared at the rate of four pairs a year until he was twenty-one. Leo got bored with this long-winded, drawn out situation. 'I will try my own way,' he said.

Dancing was becoming very popular, especially the new waltz from Vienna. Leo engaged a dance teacher to come and give him the basics. In the seclusion of his own drawing room he fancied he was becoming very adept, so he asked his father to organise a ball at their ancestral home.

He had no idea if this venture would work, but across the room he selected a tall, strong female with a pleasant enough face, but rather weathered like an outdoor girl. That's an asset, not a disadvantage, he calculated, so with no hesitation, he strode deliberately up to her.

They started with a minuet, he knew the steps of that much older dance, next followed the sailor's hornpipe, he knew that too. Then, just as expected, the Viennese waltz. He flung her round and round, reversing and progressing, it was hectic, energetic and exhilarating. When the music stopped they paused just long enough to compliment each other on their steps. They did it again and again. She still looked very cool, but Leo, who always ate too much anyway, was perspiring profusely.

'Let's miss the next one,' he said – but the lady insisted, so off they went again, this time a polka.

The energy that dancing demands does not compare with the few steps he had mastered alone in the drawing room. He had no idea that the polka was so formidable and arduous so when the clock reached half past eleven he suggested they should retire gracefully. Although he would not admit it, even to himself, this was the first time that anyone, male or female, had overtaken his stamina. He had of course been using muscles never before stretched. Exercise was second nature to him, but not dancing. If ever he had been truly happy it was today.

Henry stayed up late into the night peering into *Who's Who*. This must be nipped in the bud if her ancestry could not be found there. At last it was; she was the daughter of an army officer from the borders.

Both were up early next day to walk the moors, Leo's muscles were stiff but he concealed the fact from his new-found friend. 'I'll take you to a special place,' he said. 'It's my favourite spot'. So up they went to the viewpoint. She marvelled at the fissured limestone, then he turned her around slowly. 'All this will be mine one day,' he announced. 'Can you see the hamlet down there?'

*She has pride, ambition and resolve; her wealth and station are good. That's perfect, why am I waiting?* His mind was tormenting him. If this was love, he had no idea; it had never crossed his mind.

'Will you marry me?' he proposed to her in clear confident tones.

'Yes,' she answered and his first kiss hovered gently onto her lips.

# — 4 —

# Necessary requisitions

With jaunty steps they descended the moors; neither mentioned the agreement they had just pledged. Leo insisted that Mary – now they used Christian names – stayed an extra night and he personally would drive her home the following day. All members of staff recognised the situation immediately. This was the first applicant that had stayed two nights and was the first to be taken home by Lord Leo.

Even Henry knew that this one would be going home with no gloves. When they left the next morning Mary shook hands correctly from the highest down to the lowest. The staff all waved, knowing for certain that she would be returning. Back they went to the kitchen, compliments and praises, approvals and cheers were resounding. One voice did proffer the fact that she appeared rather cold, only dismissed immediately, because they knew that that temperament would be reciprocated. They unanimously agreed, 'A perfect match.'

After reaching her home, introductions were made and Leo requested a private meeting with her father. He offered Leo a cigar, which he accepted gratefully. He did not admit that he had never smoked one before; so he tried in vain to puff if. If it was meant to relieve the tension, it did nothing of the sort. There was no tension; he had come here with the predetermined intention to ask for his daughter's hand in marriage. Why would anyone be nervous? This is just one reality that must be faced once in a lifetime.

Formalities over, Leo and Mary drove to the jewellers to purchase the engagement ring set with one solitary diamond. All arranged to meet again to start wedding discussions. The pair knew that both would always be faithful, because they were each heading towards expected goals. She would receive a titled husband with many servants; he, in turn, would receive many sons.

They knew very little about each other, but life would continue exactly as it had during the past generations. He gave her a butterfly kiss as he mounted the homeward-bound carriage.

Henry was prepared to give Leo another set of rules. First, no endearments should ever be heard or seen in public, especially in the proximity of the staff. Next, behaviour must be both upright and rigid, even after the ceremony; all advances must be behind closed doors. 'I will not tolerate any lowering of standards in this household. I will not face such embarrassment.'

The wedding was now discussed. The distaff side should provide the wedding breakfast, but, highly commended and respected as this family was, it did not boast those vital, crucial, patriotic genes. Leo therefore, approached the family and was well received; they were very willing to leave all responsibilities and organisation to Henry. Moira took no part; she was often unwell and suffered from a lack of confidence, aggravated by her humiliation.

The ceremony would be at their own church. Both bride and groom would wear cheviot tweeds of supreme quality and even Mary's hat would be of a matching tweed. Leo had recently inherited part ownership of a coal mine so resources were as bottomless as the pit he owned.

Wines and whiskies were ordered in abundance, two extra cooks were engaged, and the whole feast would be prepared in their own kitchen. The menu included Scottish salmon, unrestricted sirloins of beef from Aberdeen Angus bullocks, fruits, cream cheeses, and sweetmeats. All the staff received new uniforms, including the extra newly appointed butler.

Maybe a bit lavish Henry thought, but I've only got one son and no daughters. Everything was ordered with no frills or trimmings, just solid, substantial and necessary accessories.

The service was held early in the day, according to plan, and there were no hitches. There were none of those useless tears shed at the service either. When at the end of the service the groom was told he could kiss the bride, he made no movement. Mary reached forward and kissed him on the cheek. So, man and wife – by that piece of paper alone – they left the church together. The banquet was perfect including the drinks. So much did they drink that it was not even noticed when the bride and groom went missing. They had put on their brogues and after deciding that too much alcohol was being consumed by too few mouths, they walked up to their viewpoint. There, in view of the whole world yet seen by no one, they had their first passionate kiss. It had been secretly planned without the knowledge of anyone, least of all Leo's father.

They were experiencing that mystical inward swelling of pride, oblivious to all their guests. The question of where they should live did not arise. This mansion had been well prepared for the last generation yet only served one pupil. Mary knew her role, to give him sons that in turn would reproduce those cultured, priceless noble genes.

They would start their honeymoon on the following day, leaving in their carriage and pair for Exmoor. Leo had engaged his own footman and they would travel in stages, changing horses at well-established coaching inns. When, however, they retired for their first night, Henry had contrived to offer them two adjoining single bedrooms, to make doubly sure they had a good night's rest before travelling.

# Patience is rewarded

Every member of the household rose early the next morning; each performed his or her own allotted chore. The honeymoon couple were equal to the challenge; they had, by the predetermined cunning of Henry, slept in separate rooms, which they had casually accepted. 'If you buy a gun licence, you don't have to go shooting immediately,' they calculated, 'so this new licence can wait until a more favourable opportunity emerges.'

They were to travel alone except for the footman and a lady's maid. Leo knew the location of each coaching inn. He had travelled the same route several times with Henry.

They faced the elements at dawn; blankets, furs, food and whisky were packed to bolster the long journey. They would make three stops where horses were changed, food and drink stocks were replenished and at one inn they would stay the night. The landlord apologised for having no bridal suite but offered them comfortable feather beds with strong horse-hair foundations, in separate rooms. He wished them well and a restful night.

They rose very early, anxious, and eager to resume their journey, but although the days were long, when they arrived at their destination, the sun was already beginning to set. Travelling had increased both tiredness and exhaustion, so that when their room was offered they did not register the twin beds with pretty quilts standing parallel about six feet apart.

After a quick toilet, each in their own room, they went down for the evening meal. They excused themselves and retired immediately literally collapsing into their own beds and dropping into deep sleep.

On waking Leo was quite ashamed as he had neither kissed Mary nor wished her a good night, but he refrained from mentioning the fact. He did, however, contrive to speak to his valet asking if the beds could be put just a little closer together. 'As you please sir,' he replied. Mary had also decided to approach the lady's maid. 'Will you enter into a deep scheme with me?' she asked. 'When we are out during the day would you mind putting the beds just a little nearer together?'

So, during the day, to the amusement and merriment of the staff, each bed was given that tempting push, and behold they were side by side.

Their daytime walks on the springy moors were enjoyed by both, watching for deer or herons or buzzards by the ever-bubbling streams. They were at one with nature; they walked the coast and scraggy banks. They battled over the scree and through the strangled oaks. This was their most physical occupation and they revelled in it.

Back in their bedroom they were surprised, even shocked; neither had expected their request to be taken so literally. They were both in an embarrassing situation, because, inwardly they were each taking the responsibility for it. They could not even smile, though I think the staff made up for that!

When they had undressed and emerged from their cubicles they stood like reluctant swimmers shivering on the brink, not daring to take the plunge. They knelt by the adjacent beds to say their prayers. The words could not be heard so whether they were 'Give me courage' or 'Watch over me' can only be guessed. So, on the fourth night of their marriage, their predestined life started. This was the planned future already mapped out for them; the ice had been broken, they must now prove themselves. This was the only reason for their existence.

Enjoyment did not enter into the situation; this was a means to an end and the end must be reached. There was no love, no intimacy, no petting and no coaxing. Those qualities belonged to the frivolous servants who had no real identity in life; their stock was irrelevant, it was a game to them, 'five minute fun' they called it. Should their genes become extinct, the nation would not suffer. They were the dead wood of the human species, useful only as servants, courted only as soldiers. They were viewed as the necessary obstacles of life.

The following day the horses were harnessed and Leo and Mary took a drive around some of the beautiful places of Exmoor. They looked across the Bristol Channel, crawled up and down steep hills carved out by water torrents and stopped for a snack at an inn to sample the local cider. They crossed one stream on stepping stones, holding hands in a chivalrous, courteous way, while the carriage and pair crossed through the torrent.

During that day those 'necessary obstacles' at the inn were preparing a venison evening meal. Their light-hearted jokes concerning the previous night kept them amused all day. They were all convinced that the scheme had worked, certain in fact, because they had all taken spells at the keyhole.

# — 6 —

# Disappointments

After a fortnight exploring Exmoor the couple returned via the coaching inns. They had enjoyed each other's company in one of the most beautiful parts of the country. Their ultimate mission, they hoped, was accomplished but they must wait a few weeks to be sure.

On returning Mary took complete charge of the day-to-day running of the household. The reallocation of the staff duties as there was now one extra to be catered for. Each day the menu was debated and discussed with the cook. Mary was competent; her stature demanded authority. She was never severe and appeared to understand those lesser mortals; she praised each when the occasion arose.

She did not neglect her walks with Leo; their upright, rigid figures strode at considerable pace, with golden retrievers abounding nearby. 'Let's go to the viewpoint,' she said, 'I'm feeling so energetic today.'

A keen, east wind was blowing, but it went unnoticed. Then, in factual, predictable tones, more appropriate to documentary evidence than to romantic news, she announced; 'Your first son is on his way.' Leo really expected the news – after all he had started the ball rolling – but even so he was thrilled and delighted. They were on the threshold of a new life. He could not contain his elation; he threw his arms around her and kissed her passionately.

For the present there would be no changes in their country life; there would be walks each day but that was usual, there would be the very best food available, but that too was usual.

After about two months, the news broke. Most pleased was Henry, Moira was getting weaker, but she still wanted her son to be happy. Leo was treated as Henry's son; Moira secretly thought that mothers should also be credited.

Mary carried this pregnancy with typical ease, rarely discussing it. She

25

took on the refurbishment of the nursery, she organised the nurses, no wet nurse was approached. 'I will be feeding my own baby,' she stated. 'That is my clear cut prerogative.' Leo took this meekly. He knew very little about babies, but he was keen to assure her that money should not be considered. On this issue, her decision was final.

All preparations for the event were made systematically. There were to be no upheavals in their family life. Leo rarely enquired after Mary's health; after all she was just doing her duty to him. This was to be the first of many such events. He gave her a routine kiss each night before she retired to her own room ensuring her sleep would be undisturbed.

Late in the spring when the lambs were frisking, the birds were nesting and peewits were screaming overhead, Mary likewise produced her first offspring after a comparatively short labour.

'You have a beautiful, perfect, eight-pound daughter,' the nurse announced to Leo. He pretended to be pleased, but to make sure of another arrival at some time in the future, he enquired about the health of his wife.

'Perfectly all right, no complications, quite an easy birth,' came the reply.

He decided to be tolerant, so on his first visit to Mary he kissed her and congratulated her. She in turn apologised. 'A son next time,' she promised. Mary was expecting to choose names for daughters, but as Leo was somewhat disappointed she offered the choice to him. Without any hesitation he opted for Patience. He would look at her and repeat her name each time he felt aggrieved.

Mary was as great a success with breast-feeding as she was with the pregnancy. The nurse undertook all other baby chores, nappy changing and so on.

Henry came to view the infant and knew why Leo had chosen the name Patience.

Mary carried on breast-feeding for a whole year, thinking that when Leo decided to renew his quest for a son, it would protect her for a few extra months. But by the time Patience was toddling around the nursery, Mary was aware that another brother or sister was on its way.

She had no idea how to ensure a son; the doctor could nor help her either. 'If it proves to be another daughter I will name her Pandora. Hope will see us through.'

Exactly two years after the birth of Patience, Pandora came into the world. Leo was clearly frustrated and it showed. The staff avoided him, but the butler decided to give him some quiet suggestions.

When Leo's anger was subsiding, the butler tried to sympathise with him. 'You are very disappointed, my lord.'

'I am indeed,' came the reply.

'Well sir, I'll tell you what Tom the blacksmith did. He had three daughters, and like you, he didn't know whether to blame himself or his wife. So, when he gets into bed the next time, he takes off his nightshirt. Yes, he was bare, right down to his birthday suit, but it did the trick. Then he gets three sons.'

The butler could never have imagined a situation when he would talk to his lordship in this way, he was used to such idle chat in the kitchen. If the blacksmith had actually found an answer to this worldly problem, perhaps it would change the fortune of his lordship. He really did feel sorry for him.

# Credible and incredible reasons

As he contemplated the next addition to the family, Leo thought seriously about the suggestion offered by his butler. He would attempt anything, however absurd, to get a son and to ensure that the blame for failure did not fall upon him.

Mary was completely engrossed in breast-feeding Pandora and talking and walking with Patience; she took her pleasure in the simple things a two-year-old can do. Physically, Patience was a strong character very similar to her mother; she walked a considerable distance without tiring. In her heart, Mary would sincerely love to find a way of ensuring that the next offspring would be male.

It was on Patience's third birthday that Mary suggested taking her to the viewpoint. Leo had not been for some time but a walk with Mary would relieve the worry that depressed him. As they walked they had a heart-to-heart conversation as to who was the cause of their situation. Mary suggested that she should leave the babies next Sunday and they would both go to matins; she had found it very difficult while carrying and nursing.

'Let us make an ardent plea, then have faith that God will see fit to give us a son.' They prayed together a mutual prayer, but Mary always concluded with the words, 'If it be Thy will.'

So they entered into the third attempt with prayers on their lips; but for Leo, nothing on his body. They prayed weekly in Church, nightly at each bedside, and quietly each hour of the day. Mary pondered the next name if it should prove to be a daughter.

'It will be Grace,' she mused. 'Yes, she will certainly be sent by the love of God.'

The name was now mapped out and prearranged. Mary enjoyed being pregnant, she loved breast-feeding and tutoring the young; she was most

The Three Horseshoes at Long Hanborough. The garage at the rear was the stables at the time of the book.

certainly not tiring of being broody and giving life or being responsible for the small infants. She had been sent to Leo for this purpose, of that she was certain.

Patience, now just four years old, was so pleased when Grace arrived. Leo was not so pleased. He was becoming desperate, he was beside himself with anger. 'I've done my best,' he uttered aloud. 'The fault must be with Mary.'

'I'll go away for a few days,' he was suggesting to himself. He called the footman and ordered the horses to be harnessed. He had decided to return to Exmoor for the stag hunt. He would be away for two or three weeks and took his gun and his rifle, but it was the first time he had gone without his father. It was 1850.

Leo met up with his brothers at the family's London home, Syon House, and travelled to Exmoor from there. He stopped at the coaching inns as usual, the last of which was The Three Horseshoes in Long Hanborough in Oxfordshire (another brother regularly stopped at The Sun in Begbroke). Long Hanborough was then on the direct route from London to the west. Coaching inns benefited accordingly. The new A40

29

was not built for another hundred years. As he drew up a small unkempt seven-year-old girl offered to hold the halter on the horses. Her father was inside doing cellar work. Emma had no mother; her father, George, would not allow her to go into the workhouse. When the owner of the horses stepped out of the carriage, Emma knew she would be given at least one penny.

The stag hunt lasted a fortnight before Leo started the return journey. He had enjoyed his hunting, he was skilled with both gun and rifle. They stopped at the same inn when returning and there was Emma ready to hold the horses again. There was a note inside, from his wife, just stating that all was well and they hoped to greet him home soon. Leo, feeling more relaxed, gave Emma two pennies, 'Thank you, thank you, my lord,' she said, bobbing up and down as she had been taught.

'I will do this each year,' he promised himself, 'when I am weary with the monotony of bonnets and petticoats.'

Mary welcomed him home, thinking that a restart and change of scenery for Leo might predict a change of sex. This was like turning over a new leaf, or the rising of the sun each day. 'If the next baby should be a girl, I will name her Dawn.'

Nothing had changed. Dawn, true to her name, arrived very early one morning. Now someone had to be courageous enough to tell Leo, but he had already convinced himself that it would be a girl. Life to him was like a blank cartridge, so, in anticipation, he had already prepared for another trip to Exmoor.

No one objected to him going, as he was becoming a loner, deep in thought, like a child that could not have his favourite toy. He spotted Emma as before at The Three Horseshoes. She was pleased to see him as those pennies were such a blessing. Leo carried on to the stag hunt but was recalled very quickly as the health of his mother, Moira, had suddenly deteriorated. Moira's life was ebbing away; sadly she had never had a grandson, and Henry was now beginning to doubt the possibility.

## — 8 —

# Emma's Oxfordshire home

We leave Leo and his family briefly to visit the home of George and his seven-year-old daughter. My mother had described Emma's home in detail to me; I managed to locate it by obtaining a birth certificate. There was just one difference; mother had said that there was no path to the door, just a track made by horses' hooves. Now there was a clean concrete drive.

I was well prepared but it still came as a shock to me. I guessed it would be fairly dilapidated and tumbled down, but my expectations were proved wrong. The whole building stood exactly as strong as the day it was built, probably five hundred years earlier.

The walls were stone built, very wide and strong. The robust well seasoned oak trusses that held up the roof were as perfect as when they were placed. The roof itself was heavy and slated with Stonesfield slate, but equally well preserved.

Certain points stood out, the wooden doors now rotted and gone had left very wide doorways. There was a loft, but the ladder or outside steps had disappeared. There were no flues or chimneys, no window, just a small hole for ventilation. The party walls inside were only about six feet high, so obviously no privacy. There was nothing left of either ceilings or floors. I was in fact looking at an architecturally designed stable block. No expense was spared for such necessary members of a rich family life.

Agricultural workers were necessary, but they could easily be replaced at a moment's notice. Horses were the only means of transport, and such valuable friends of the family must be well housed and protected. The loft would hold hay and straw, so that in the event of a hard winter the horses would be kept well fed and bedded.

I did step inside the small room that had no ventilation hole. This was the actual room where my ancestors were born. It did have a comparatively

31

new stable door, and it appeared to have recently housed a pony.

It was a cold but sunny winter day when I was there, and the temperature inside was very warm. It resembled the atmosphere of a cave, very equable, both warm in winter and cool in summer.

How could such a building be adapted from the use of animals to humans? Such a building was actually an asset to a poor family. With all winds and weathers eliminated, warmth was appreciated. Even so, there were vital drawbacks. Light was so restricted that it was necessary to sleep and rise with the sun.

There were no visible means of cooking; would they light a fire on stones, enabling them to cook a rabbit stew? I do not know, but there was no escape for smoke and the floor was carpeted with straw.

Horses do not need lavatories, so no such amenity existed; they dug a hole outside at the back of the building and that served for all. When full, another turf was cut to cover it and the new one used. Toilet paper? Horses don't need that either. Did they copy the Romans? The mind boggles… Flies multiplied in the summer and rats came in for warmth in the winter. Water was provided in a trough for the animals and that was always available if it was not frozen. Their personal toilet must leave a lot to the imagination.

Even under these conditions women could expect to give birth every two years. They always breast fed as long as possible in the belief that it hindered another pregnancy.

George Ashton was my great great grandfather. He had been tempted to leave Kirtlington in 1832 at the age of 22 for this house and the job on the farm. They were expecting their first baby but both his wife Rebecca and the new infant daughter died in childbirth. After about two years, he remarried in 1839, this time to a Freeland girl named Elizabeth. Her first baby died aged about two but she was already expecting another.

Things now went horribly wrong. George had an accident on the farm, which resulted in a broken leg. It was logical to think that he could no longer work as a farm labourer, so he and his family must be prepared to leave. His brother took his job and living area, and in sympathy he offered the end room to George and his wife.

The next baby arrived in 1843 – this was Emma, a very strong, robust baby who appeared to be immune from all the germs and bugs that

John's birth certificate does not give his father's name.

inhabited the place. The pain in George's leg improved and he began to shuffle around. It was determination alone that began to make him more mobile.

When Emma was two years old another baby arrived in that stable. As so often happened, mother and baby died in childbirth. One speculates

George and Emma lived in the stable on the far left, part of the stable block at Bowles Farm. It was about six feet wide and ten feet deep. John and his sister were born here. The other stables also housed families.

why, when they lived so adjacent to death, they should strive to produce so many babies. The object of birth is to pass on one's genes but there were then so many losers.

George viewed his situation, a fairly young man, with an inflexible leg and no hope of rewarding employment, having lost two wives and three babies, living in an unheated stable, with one strong two-year-old daughter.

The workhouse would have taken them both, but they would have been parted. Although friends and family encouraged it, George stood firm. 'I would never see Emma again,' he speculated. 'I am determined to persevere.'

So each day father and daughter supported each other to the Three Horseshoes in Long Hanborough. This was a muddy trek of about three miles. George knew they would be treated well by the landlord. He could still harness and un-harness the horses of customers, picking up a few welcome coppers. Emma, forever hungry, was tempted with leavings from the plates.

If they had eaten sufficient to fight hunger until the next day, they went home happy. 'Take no thought for the morrow,' was his comment and he believed it literally because he had no option. When arriving home they collapsed on the straw in the corner of the stable and slept till sunrise.

Emma's scraggy, feeble body and grubby cheeky smile, always just lurking ready to break out, endeared her to all. Both of them benefited from the hospitality and mutual goodwill that was activated by her personality.

'We are not beggars or tramps, are we?' she would question her father.

'No,' he would answer, 'We are just parasites.'

She did not understand, but at least she thought they were not on the bottom rung of the ladder.

# — 9 —

# Worlds apart

Back in the north, the loss of Leo's mother did not dissuade either Leo or Mary in their mission for a son.

Mary lavished love on all her daughters, she employed an extra house-keeper just to wash and iron all the frilly frocks and cotton bonnets.

'I will always love each one, and the next will therefore have a name that means love.' Charity was the chosen name. Would she ever bear a son? This possibility was beginning to creep into her mind, she was becoming resigned to it.

So many infants caused much extra work but a tutor had already been engaged for the oldest children. Each was developing her own individual character. Mary kept a diary of all events in the household; this included likes and dislikes, coughs and sneezes, comments by the servants, indeed any point that would help her remember and keep consistent discipline.

One particular day she had been called away and the diary was acci-dentally left open on her desk. The recently employed housekeeper yielded to temptation and glanced at it. Yesterday's entry said 'Mrs A, very grumpy'. She thought about it, and being inquisitive, she approached the kitchen staff with her secret knowledge.

'You shouldn't be a nosy-parker,' they said. 'You of course are Mrs A.'

She never lived down the tease and ridicule of the other servants, but she now knew that Mary registered and noted every detail.

After several months, Charity came along. The birth was uneventful, Leo didn't even look at the baby, as he had expected a girl, so he chose to act indifferently. Mary was as pleased as before, her health and strength was coping with the rigours of childbirth and an active demanding family.

As before Leo took the easy way out and the familiar route to Exmoor. Calling at the Three Horseshoes he again saw Emma who was now eleven

36

years old. She was fast growing up; the poverty she endured and the hours she worked had resulted in a thin, scraggy child who was perpetually hungry.

She was always cheerful and friendly to customers. She had long ago discovered that their generosity depended on it, and that she depended upon their generosity. She curtsied a little better now and she could harness or un-harness their horses; she would willingly tackle any job. She knew in her heart that she would soon be sent into gentlemen's service in Oxford; she did not anticipate this with any pleasure. Life would be such a contrast, hours would be long and arduous, it would be severe and harsh; young girls were easily exploited. Sometimes, employers were cruel bullies.

Leo patted her tangled locks, gave her the expected reward, then mounted his carriage and was gone. As he travelled south he thought about his unusual family. His mother had been small and weak yet she had given birth to one strong, robust son. Because of this fact, he had chosen a strong well-developed female, yet all he had or seemed likely to have was girls born in uninterrupted succession. It was an unbroken line, as certain as the steps in a staircase. How he wished they would reach a landing.

The thought of different company and a good hunt kept his mind from the echoing, haunting topic. When he retraced his route northwards, he found the family and household all in perfect order. It was as if he was neither needed nor wanted. The girls hardly knew him as father.

Mary tried to raise his spirits. 'We will have one more attempt,' she pacified him.

'It will only be another female,' he grunted.

'Be that as it may, we must both accept the situation. We will have lots of grandsons,' she tried to reconcile him.

'My name will be gone,' he said, 'and that is either your fault or mine.'

The baby took a little longer to conceive this time; so, to coincide with the stag shooting season, he actually left her while she was carrying the sixth child; he knew he would be home before the event.

Stopping at The Three Horseshoes on his way to Exmoor he saw Emma again, but this time she had on a white apron and was pulling pints behind the bar. She had sampled private service in Oxford but ran away to regain her freedom. How could an eleven-year-old country girl dovetail into gentlemen's service? A girl who had never used a knife and fork, never had a bath or brushed her hair, never used a lavatory, yet was expected to toe the line immediately. She had now learnt to wash her face, brush her hair and wear a white apron that belonged to the pub.

Now, at the age of thirteen, service well behind her, she was promoted to a presentable barmaid.

# — 10 —

# Unforgivable sin

So it came about, just before the beginning of the closed season for stag hunting, that Leo started his homeward journey and the first stop again was The Three Horseshoes.

On his arrival, Emma offered him a letter that had come a few days earlier. She curtsied as she gave it to him, completely misjudging the reaction that it would spark. The letter like a telegram stated:

*To Leo and Mary, a daughter, premature but both mother and baby well. Her name is Faith.*

He sank into a chair; the bottom was out of his world. 'Whisky!' he demanded and Emma took it to him. He gulped it down, still trying to absorb the meaning of the note. 'She still has faith,' he was muttering audibly, 'It's all her fault, that is obvious. I've been tricked. Another whisky!' That one was swallowed so quickly that it soon caught up with the first. He rose, pacing the taproom. His anger and temper were unrestrained and rampant. His line of ancestry would now be broken. His whole purpose in life was shattered.

'I've got health and strength, money and estate, and a title entrusted to me. Give me just one, please?' he implored, yet his footman alone knew the cause of the outburst.

He turned to face Emma to request more whisky, then in a flash he said, 'You could do better than this, couldn't you?'

'Yes, my lord, yes, my lord,' she answered, quite unaware of what he meant.

He whipped her into his arms and carried her laughing and willing into the unknown.

'Now we'll see,' he muttered as he carried her up the stone stairs.

When they came downstairs later, Emma was visibly shaking through her whole body, but in the palm of her hand she was clutching a shiny half

39

crown. She had never owned such a coin; it was more than her father could earn in a week. In her innocence she had poured oil on his outburst. He slumped, or more correctly lay nearly prostrate in the chair. The journey, the whisky and the sex had all contributed to his state of unconsciousness.

Emma was not sure if she should discuss the situation with the landlady, but ultimately she said, 'All he wants is a son. He is willing to pay me well if I have a boy.'

'I've heard those stories before,' came the reply. 'You are now a prostitute, and you must live with that knowledge.'

'I don't object to that, if it gives both my dad and me enough to eat. My dad has protected me well; now it's my turn to help us both,' Emma reasoned.

'You are living in a fool's paradise,' suggested the landlady, but innocent optimism was ruling Emma's thoughts.

Next day the carriage and pair headed north. Before leaving, Leo sought out Emma and demanded the son should be called John. 'I will always support him,' he assured her, 'I will never ever let him down.'

Although still feeling thwarted, Leo felt there could still be a successful outcome. It would not, indeed could not be shared, but was a mere thread to which he would secretly cling.

The abruptness and positiveness of his character had been dealt a blow. His anger now subsided, he was behaving as if squashed like a defeated army, or deflated balloon.

But this one grain of comfort, this one crumb of hope, was helping to keep his whole being balanced and stabilised against everything that his family, nature or God could bring to bear on him. He was clutching at straws, refusing to be beaten.

# Some you win, some you lose

Leo arrived home deflated, Mary was expecting an outrage but he was so subdued and self-controlled it was difficult for her to understand him. He admired his daughters from a distance. There was no love; just respect for Mary's achievement. Patience was now ten years old, just three years younger than the Emma he had left at The Three Horseshoes.

His daughters were pretty little girls but Emma was a tool to use or cast aside at his discretion. 'If she has any sense at all she will produce a son. How privileged to be the mother of my son,' he mused.

Mary, so touched by his placid manner, offered to try again. 'It would be the seventh, could be very lucky,' she suggested.

He refused. 'No, I will not submit you to the stress and strain again; the pressure has already turned my father into an old man.'

After waiting a few months, the weather not being too severe, he decided to return to Exmoor for just a few days. His real intention was to discover the condition of Emma. He was getting somewhat impatient but could not share his secret, nor must he show any sign of nervousness.

It was nearing Christmas 1856 when Leo next appeared at The Three Horseshoes. Emma was still there, working hard, but there was a natural glow in her cheeks and her thin, frail, but very wiry body could not hide the forthcoming event. She looked pleased but he was ecstatic. He ordered a whisky and overpaid her, telling her to keep the change. Even the horses seemed exhilarated and more fleet of foot as they steered the carriage to Exmoor. But he only stayed a few days, his mind was not adjusted to hunting; he was keen to start his homeward journey.

Leo arranged payment for Emma with the landlord of The Three Horseshoes. 'You are to allocate her two shillings and sixpence each week. If the baby is a boy, the money is to be paid without interruption but should it be a girl, you will stop it immediately.'

Emma knew exactly what was happening, but whether it was hope, faith, or just plain confidence, she felt she was on to a good thing.

On the fifteenth of February eighteen hundred and fifty seven, John Ashton was born. This small, fourteen-year-old girl produced a very large son. She had no help from anyone except her father, who was useless apart from ardent, fruitful, praying. The isolated stable at Bowles Farm in Freeland was now the home of John whose mother was the poorest yet father the richest in the land.

There were no complications, baby was strong and fed well. Emma's father now busied himself, collecting the weekly money and making sure that Emma was well fed. The baby flourished, a bouncing, strapping lad; Emma's inborn maternal instinct had boosted her ego, she loved her baby and the regular money had eliminated all the worries of survival.

George, her father, still worked at the pub but Emma could not return until the baby was able to walk.

One day, George came home in the carriage that belonged to Leo. It had been sent to take both mother and child to the pub for Leo's approval. He admired and welcomed the contented, huge baby. *He has my features and one day, I hope, my stature and estate.*

Emma was completely satisfied. She knew she was not the decision-maker for him.

'He must attend school regularly, the fees will be prepaid,' ordered Leo. No poor people could ever afford to educate their offspring, so the locals were questioning where this bastard child had come from.

Leo called at the pub at least twice a year to oversee the upbringing of his son. He was secretly making comparisons between his son and his daughters. They were as chalk and cheese. The daughters living in luxury, the son in extreme poverty.

When John was three years old, Leo approached Emma and suggested a second son. In her innocence, she was very willing; she could see nothing wrong, never had a poor girl been so well treated.

'Terms exactly as before,' Leo said. 'The boy will be called George. No upkeep money if it is a girl.'

Although John was now old enough to talk with his father, Leo dictated that he was not to be told. 'He is not to call me father; I am his benefactor now, and let's keep it that way.'

The second pregnancy was as easy as the first, and extra money was waiting each week. The prospect was good… but the new infant was female so the money stopped immediately.

Leo was not interested, he did not even look at the babe, didn't ask of her health or offer schooling fees.

Emma did not bother to register the birth; no reason to do so if there was no financial reward. She did, however, have her christened – Georgina – thereby making doubly sure there was no obstacle to prevent her entry into the Kingdom of Heaven.

# — 12 —

# Goodbye Henry

It was at this time that Emma was given a nice cottage in Freeland with a very large garden. It was called Chapel House. How she came by the house one can only imagine, but it was a big leap from a stable to house ownership. As the garden was so large, George acquired a cow – where did that come from? – he could milk it and take it along the roads to munch grass.

Emma was disappointed that she received no money for Georgina's upkeep, but she had put herself in that position; her optimism had excluded it from her thoughts.

'It's like tossing a coin,' she mused. 'Sometimes it's heads, sometimes it's tails.'

Emma loved babies, and like most mothers had inwardly craved for a daughter. She accepted her lot without a grumble; John had already started school so Georgina would not be deprived of either motherly love or time.

Back at his estate Leo was keeping up the pretence of at least being interested in the upbringing of his daughters. Like other wealthy fathers, he purchased a pianoforte and decided they should all have the chance to become proficient musicians. Knowing very little about music or composers, he would listen to others and then consider he could converse on the subject. He insisted on listening to their party pieces each week. The piece he used as a standard was Beethoven's 'Für Elise'. He thought when they could master that they were several steps up the ladder of success. The truth was that none of them were really interested. They had never been taken to concerts and neither parent understood the value of music.

Patience did enjoy playing hymns and even insisted on playing them, although she knew it irritated her father. When she stopped playing, she sang them perpetually; Leo was infuriated, Patience knew, but she was indifferent to his moods.

She was now fifteen and had developed an independent personality. She would listen to her father; but after much thought, she would make her own decisions and act accordingly.

Pandora, now thirteen, had no time for music. She liked walking, spending her whole life outside, and was often seen helping the gardener. She could think freely outside, converse with the footman, even make witty remarks. She was not going to succumb or knuckle under to such a narrow, confined regime.

Grace loved reading. It was her method of opting out of her surroundings. Although only eleven years old she had read all the books that had been placed in the library by her grandfather. She loved poetry and in her childish way had started to write a few verses.

Mary loved each one and encouraged their individuality.

Whether keen or not, they all attended matins now; both parents considered they were setting a good example to the parishioners. Even Henry went but his spirits were very low, having no grandson.

The Freeland cottage today. The extension to the left was originally John's dairy.

Leo was sorry for his father, and decided to give him a boost, so when they were enjoying a cigar together, he told him about John.

'When he is twenty-one, I shall bring him home,' he said. 'I can then take him to the viewpoint.'

'You can't do that,' his father retorted, 'You must wait for a grandson.'

'But a grandson will not bear our name,' groaned Leo.

'Neither does the other lad,' his father said. 'He bears the name of his mother.'

The topic ceased suddenly or there would have been a family quarrel. The knowledge had sunk deep into the elderly man. He sat quietly contemplating what might have been. He had been thwarted, his son had been thwarted, but Leo had chosen the disreputable way out of the situation.

'What happened to the gardener's daughter?' Henry asked himself. He remembered expelling her from the hamlet for the same offence. 'Am I now being punished?' he pondered as the thoughts went round and round in his head. His willpower and determination were failing daily; only a faint-hearted regression was taking its place. So Henry departed this life at the age of sixty-five with failure written all over his face. His son had disgraced him.

Leo kept up his jaunts to Exmoor. As well as letting him see John, they took him away from the home where he felt so lonely, surrounded by females.

## — 13 —

# Kicking the traces

Leo knew it was his responsibility to match his six daughters with partners in the same relative position. What a task! Although he knew very little about them, their likes and dislikes, their abilities or characters, he still put his faith in the breed stock.

He was marshalling the necessary items for a ball. This was strictly for Patience as she neared her eighteenth birthday. He rarely saw her now; she seemed to be spending her time walking the moors, alone, engrossed in her own thoughts. Without the knowledge of her father, she was frequently calling at the church to confide in her maker and ask his guidance.

Sometimes these profound prayers were on her own behalf but often it was heartfelt intercession, knowing the plight of the majority. 'How can I possibly help?' she beseeched. 'Please give me some direction.'

At last the inspiration came, she would give up her own life and enter a convent; she would become a 'sister of mercy'. This was to be her life, her choice; the way ahead was narrow but she was resolute, she was positive.

Mary just patted her head when Patience confided in her, then they said a prayer together to ensure the decision was correct.

When Leo told Patience of the forthcoming ball, she coolly explained that in a few days she would be entering the convent and leaving her home, her family and all her worldly wealth behind her. Leo was stunned; he was unapproachable. What had Mary done wrong, to put this ridiculous notion into her head. He did not speak to Patience again; when she offered her hand to say 'goodbye' he refused it, but it did not worry her. After eighteen years she did not understand her father or his direction in life.

Pandora was so different, no silly ideas in her head, walking the dogs on the moors, helping the groom or the gardener. She was so assured and positive, she wanted an outdoor life. She needed to do physical things, picking apples or harvesting potatoes, she loved every aspect of nature.

Between the ages of sixteen and eighteen she was spending more and more time in the garden. A mutual understanding had developed between her and the gardener's son. No one had their eyes open to what was happening; not even the pair concerned.

Then, accidentally or intentionally, they met on a wet day in the potting shed.

'I am my own boss,' announced Pandora. 'I know father will be furious, he will sack you immediately. We must secretly devise a scheme to leave the hamlet.' So with Mary's knowledge, but her eyes firmly shut, a ladder was left by Pandora's window and together they eloped to Gretna Green.

Grace was a quiet, disciplined young lady. She spent hours collecting books from the library in the town, and many more reading them. She chose books on a multitude of subjects, it was her method of understanding the outside world. She had only received home tuition so knowledge of the broader aspects of life was limited and foreign to her.

She particularly enjoyed the novels of Charles Dickens. Her father knew nothing of this writer, he would not, indeed he could not, have read them. The books were having a profound influence on her outlook and character. They were also affecting her choice of acquaintances at the library. One male friend in particular was becoming very close. She knew he was popular in the nearby industrial town. She upheld his views on the political situation; they conversed fluently, their mutual understanding was progressing, as by instinct alone they each knew their destiny.

So both Leo and Mary had to learn of the pending situation. Leo searched vainly for the lad's background and it did not please him. He was indeed the son of the local mill owner, who was the Liberal member of parliament.

'I don't hold with these new-fangled names,' Leo said. 'Whigs are Whigs, and I will always call them Whigs. No Whig will ever be welcome in my home.'

Leo banned the marriage but Mary gave her blessing and Grace was wed in the local town.

Dawn was a very sociable individua; if when walking the moors she met another rambler, she always stopped to converse. She attended the local prayer meetings, because they introduced her to all the parishioners.

Sometimes they all took part in 'A Service of Song', where each confident individual chose to sing a hymn or recite a poem. Dawn usually chose a long monologue with a hidden, moral meaning. She enjoyed that and was always well applauded.

Some of the locals welcomed her friendliness and took pride in showing her their pigeons, whippets, flowers and vegetables; most of all their enormous leeks.

She pondered her life ahead. Could she devise a way of helping these ordinary people who had such a meagre existence yet were always happy and contented with their lot?

She decided to start a home for those facing hardship – orphans, the very elderly, unmarried mothers, or the victims of accidents.

'I can cook quite well, I have moderate nursing skills, I can encourage gardeners to bring along their vegetables. I can create a superb atmosphere for those willing both to give and take. It would be a friendly, homely workhouse. All would be welcome.'

She approached her father for a suitable building but was met with an emphatic 'No'. She was not deterred, but was forced to try in town.

She found a quick, positive response there, but because of the larger population, a waiting list was formed immediately – even prior to the opening. What a venture! The need was great, she was in her element.

Charity was growing up and trying out new ideas and sampling new tastes. She was beginning to worry her mother. Leo had noticed nothing unusual, but Mary knew that small amounts of whisky were frequently disappearing. She was a strong, able girl who moaned that she was bored and needed some activity. Faith loved her embroidery, but not Charity. Sometimes she was definitely intoxicated and Mary was ashamed.

When Dawn noticed Charity's plight she enticed her to her own home because there were so many deserving cases to help. Dawn coaxed her to stay, knowing there was no alcohol on the premises. So hard work and endless duties for others replaced her boredom, alcohol and sterile mind. The two sisters worked hard together, sisters in all meanings of the word.

Faith was rather frail, maybe she had been slightly spoilt by her mother but she had a loving, friendly nature. She wanted to marry and have a secure family life; nothing as positive as her older sisters. She was the only one left now, so tapestry and embroidery filled most of her hours.

When days were short and weather inclement, the salesman would call with silks and wools for her use. They became friendly – too friendly – and the inevitable happened; he disappeared and was gone, never to be seen in the district again. He was an ordinary travelling salesman who, like a sailor, had a girl in every port. Faith hid her secret for a few months but eventually confided in her mother.

'What shall I do? My father will disown me,' she forecast correctly.

'He'll not notice yet,' her mother assured her. 'Let us keep it a secret between you and me. I will help you all I can.'

She kept the secret hidden for eight months, partly because Leo had no interest in her, and partly because they rarely met.

Then, just when Faith's secret was going to be disclosed, Leo had a message to go to Oxford.

# Highs and lows

John settled into school life as a duck takes to water. He also attended the services and Sunday school at the Primitive Methodist Chapel next to his home.

Books were very scarce, the bible was used in school for scripture lessons, it was used for English lessons, and it was used for history lessons. They seemed to use it all day. What better than a passage of scripture to learn by heart or a selected passage to practise handwriting? If this was education, he loved it.

He thought the parables were clever and the miracles beyond belief. He realised that he was extremely privileged so, knowing that other boys could not read, he endeavoured to help them. They often learnt new hymns at Sunday school, many having repeated choruses. He would read them and reread them until they could all sing together. In his ignorance, he was unconsciously teaching them to read. They all anticipated their Sunday school classes with eagerness. Parents could seldom read so they encouraged their offspring to listen and learn from John.

When seven years old he had learnt so much and grown so quickly, he was as tall as his mother.

About twice each year his 'benefactor' escorted him to Witney to purchase shoes and clothes, but most of all to cultivate a mutual under-standing. They went to a hotel for a meal and he was expected to use his knife and fork correctly. His friends did not understand; their furthest journey was a walk to Hanborough.

John had a happy and secure childhood, there were no financial worries and the large garden contained vegetables, fruit trees, hens, pigs and a cow. This ensured a well-stocked larder. George lived with them, helping in every way until he died in 1870.

It was an idyllic life for John while others around him struggled to survive, many of them sadly giving up that struggle. Measles, whooping cough and tuberculosis took their toll, but all these illnesses bypassed John.

Many dads had no work, so money was short and often food as well. At that time sixty per cent of all births did not reach their tenth birthday. The average life expectancy was twenty-six years. But John's benefactor had made doubly sure that John understood that boys were stronger, more desirable and far more valuable than girls.

His friends at Sunday school were out most days, seeking anything that was useful – blackberries, mushrooms, fallen branches, or even chasing a rabbit. They sought everything and anything that could be of beneficial use.

If you managed to secure a job on the local estate, you were obliged to attend parish church services and sit in your pre-arranged pecking order. The Freeland parish church was very 'high' – the reverend was blessed with the title 'Father' and the services included the burning of incense.

This contributed to the emergence of the 'lowest' form of Methodism. While the established church was concentrating solely on the spiritual life, the Methodists were incorporating the material side as well. The primitive Methodist chapel blossomed. Nicknamed 'The Prims' it attracted the poorest, often badly fed and clothed.

Against this background the visiting preachers sought to help, especially finding sources of work. These travelling preachers received no pay, and depended on the charity of locals. They were mostly self-made small businessmen who wanted to give something back to the community. They were imitating their hero, John Wesley. They had managed to jump from the poverty trap to the pony and trap.

They were eagerly awaited at each chapel. Maybe a tree had fallen so there was wood to collect. Perhaps a farmer needed boys to drive cattle or sheep to market. John did none of these things but he did condescend to tie bundles of kindling wood to light the old tortoise stove in the chapel.

He initiated a 'Band of Hope' which would meet at the chapel on Monday evenings. Even the first meeting was packed to capacity by young and old alike. This was the start of a social activity from which they had, until now, been deprived. The old Sankey and Moody hymns rang

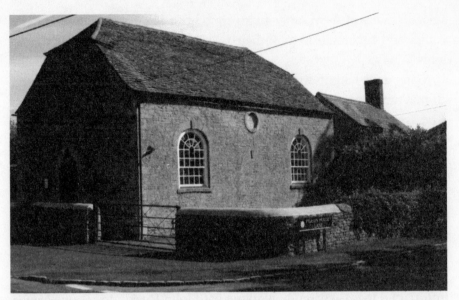

The Methodist chapel at Freeland today. John's former cottage is visible to the right.

out. They whistled and sang them for the rest of the week; they lived and worked by the words they sang.

This lifestyle continued for John until he was seventeen; then alas, he was taken very ill.

# — 15 —

# Shank's pony

Just as Faith's predicament was about to be disclosed, John in Freeland had succumbed to his first illness. So, under the false pretence of stag hunting, Leo made an extra trip to Oxfordshire. As Leo had pre-dictated, Emma had called in Dr Acland, later Sir Henry Acland but then Regius Professor of Medicine at Oxford University and Physician to the Radcliffe Infirmary. He was currently working with John Ruskin to set up science and medicine in the University alongside the classics.

John was now in the Infirmary under Dr Acland who was not optimistic about his patient. 'Even if he recovers, he will not be in perfect health, his brain may be impaired; only time will tell,' he told Leo.

Leo sat by a still and unresponsive John. He was visibly hurt, it was more than a selfish shock, he had looked forward with pleasure to the day when he would reveal himself; now that day might never come. *It must come today, my only chance.*

'I am your father,' he whispered into John's ear. There was no flicker of light, as solitary tears dropped intermittently on to the counterpane.

Dr Acland explained that John had meningitis, which very few survived. 'We must wait,' he said.

Leo determined to stay about a fortnight and each day he whispered the same words into his son's ear, 'I am your father.' Before Leo returned home there was a flicker of light in his eyes and Leo convinced himself that John understood.

All the secret hopes and expectations that he had so successfully concealed from the world for seventeen years were now shattered.

'This type of illness can definitely not be brought into our class, I can never take him to the viewpoint,' a trip he had chosen to neglect of late. 'Where is my future now?' Leo was trying to look forward.

Mary was alone in the mansion when he returned. She supervised and

Henry Acland.

organised the servants, but did little except walk her golden retriever. He was her greatest friend.

'Where is Faith?' eventually came the question.

'She has gone with her sisters, Dawn and Charity,' came the reply.

'Not another "friend of the poor" who won't help themselves when in trouble,' he jeered.

'No,' interrupted Mary, 'She is one of those who has got herself in trouble and cannot help herself. She now has a son, and will be returning home if and when you allow them both.'

Leo's mind went blank.

John, recovered from illness, returned home a changed character. He had lost his facial muscles and so showed no pleasure or even displeasure; he could not smile or even cry, those expressions had gone for ever. He had no friends, he didn't want any, but he had no enemies either. He was not capable of loving or hating. He did little work and took no pleasure, he was told not to drink alcohol, he presumed that no girl would want him so he never approached one.

He was usually alone but never lonely. Those who knew him said his interests were fizz, food and faith. He had a crate of fizzy pop stoppered with glass marbles delivered each week from Blake's of Eynsham. He recovered his usual strength and the family thought he now knew his own background – but no one ever plucked up the courage to ask him.

He ambled around the village keenly watching the skilled workmen. There were milkmen, masons, thatchers and blacksmiths. He had an uncanny way of mastering any job, laying a hedge, making a hurdle, thatching a roof or shoeing a horse. These were skills he never practised but even so he would teach and supervise young lads quite successfully and they were eager to learn.

His capabilities were never understood but he was respected by all for his knowledge. He had never specialised in anything, yet in his uncanny way, he grasped everything. He still attended 'The Prims' to put himself in a position to allocate any forthcoming job fairly and correctly. He actually did nothing for the parishioners, yet was an asset to all.

He would listen to all discussions, absorbing all angles of the topic, then he would seal off the situation with one curt statement. He would usually quote the Bible as the ultimate authority. That was final, John was never contradicted; no one would dare.

So it was, after a short winter break, forced on them by the weather, a preacher returned to 'The Prims' with some news. The only work for the past two months had been snow clearing, but now in February the forecast both for the weather and for work was better.

News had come through the chapels that many hands were needed near Hertford for drainage work where the river Lea had flooded several times. It was explained that the journey would be about eighty miles, so this determined that only the strong and able could make the trip. Men with families were encouraged not to go as they hoped to be there for several months. As boys were always available, they pleaded to go.

John listened, showing no apparent interest, but beneath that exterior, his mind was active. When the excitement had subsided, John stated his intent.

'We will leave the day after tomorrow,' he decided. 'I will take any unmarried lads who are over seventeen. You must spend tomorrow making doubly sure your boots are strong. Take two or three pairs of socks or pieces of flannel to wrap round your feet. We'll meet at this chapel at five in the morning.'

Even John, who did not show any emotion, inwardly felt excited.

He spent the next day preparing, he didn't need new boots; they were always made on a last in Witney, they never wore out. He went to Pinsley Wood, cutting stakes to make into thumb sticks. He was sure the others wouldn't think about that so he cut about a dozen. He calculated that they would walk about forty miles per day, stopping at any chapel they reached as night fell. If one of them were to twist an ankle, they would have been in trouble.

So, hair and beard cut, John, with a bundle of clothes tied like Dick Whittington, met his fellow travellers around the corner of his house at the chapel.

The limitation he had imposed had reduced the number to two. This meant that three healthy lads would be gone for many months, and they would not be competing for any jobs that arose. He issued each one with two thumb sticks, one to use and one to put over his shoulder, holding the bundle. Most of the village population was there to say goodbye and wish them well.

John did announce he would be sending postcards to the chapel. He carried the limited instructions for the route, 'Go through Oxford and head East.' They knew that they could rest and eat at any chapel on their way.

So with keen, eager faces and a sense of adventure the trek started and goodbyes were said with prayers.

The Freeland lads that had the courage to join him were Richard Jerrott and James Brakespear. Four other lads from the Long Hanborough parish went too. They were Richard Berry, James Berry, Charles Berry and Francis Pittick. Two Abingdon lads were billeted with them so I assume that they trekked with them as well.

With the light of the world to guide them they oozed courage, confidence and conviction. They journeyed into the unknown, yet carried a certain knowledge that only unquenchable faith can give. They truly depended on the Rock of Ages.

John walked slowly with long, loping strides. Only the force of gravity controlled his clumsy, ungainly body with its long, uncontrollable legs, anchored at the ends by huge, leaden boots. They were usually a source of ridicule but not any more; now they were envied. When John was walking in his slow swinging style, the others had to run or hurry to keep up with him.

They slept one night in a chapel and arrived at Hertford just after nightfall on the next day. Many more such groups were arriving, so they knew they had reached the correct destination. The following day they were directed towards the small village of Great Amwell. You'll find an inn there – The Crown – waiting to take you in and give orders.

They had left behind them pretty Oxfordshire villages, hedges, walls, ditches and small fields. They hiked down small hills and valleys, some surprise awaited them around every corner. But here there were acres of land, not a hedge, not a wall, the world stretched out for miles in front of them. The river Lea flowed slowly and silently towards the sea, trying in vain to keep within its banks.

John was called to meet other gang leaders, where they were given

The Crown Inn today, obviously greatly modernised.
Below, the view from the inn.

instructions about expectations and payment. Work was plentiful and payment to them appeared good. They worked six full days each week and the local chapel was pleased to welcome them on Sundays. That evening John sent the first of many postcards to 'The Prims' at Freeland.

John suggested the menu each day – always a fried breakfast – bacon, egg and fried bread. The evening meal was mostly based on pork; their preference being boiled fat bacon. The vegetables were put into the same pan, so when it was served, large blobs of fat were shining on the vegetables like bull's eyes staring at them.

They had never experienced such food before; they relished it. These young lads grew in stature, health, fitness and confidence. The hours of steadfast commitment and plodding endurance ensured that their bodies remained slim and lean. The work, as they saw it developing, gave them an inner satisfaction. John controlled the finances, paid the landlord and issued the lads with a weekly allowance.

The work was physically hard, but many workers were billeted in the neighbourhood and many chapels were represented. There was actually quite a social life even if it was bereft of females. The outlook was good, as many square miles needed draining.

Much of the flooding was self-inflicted. The locals had been digging peat for years to use as fuel, so now both householders and farmers were suffering.

They lodged in The Crown for eight months. They were to return home to grateful families who welcomed both their faces and their fortunes.

# — 16 —

# Life on a smallholding

While John was away, his mother Emma and his half-sister Kesiah had tended the garden and stock, milking the cow and making butter. Georgina, his sister, had already married George Franklin and left home.

Like all the other females in the village, they spent every spare moment making gloves. The local factory at Newlands in Witney kept up a good supply and they mechanically prick-seamed them. Their reward was threepence farthing for a pair, which could be completed in just over two hours.

One of the machines at the factory had been designed especially to stitch the straps on the back of military or hunting gauntlets (see the picture opposite). Not only did this machine survive a factory fire, but, after being converted to electricity it was used during the Second World War for army belts and is still operated making belts and chin straps for policemen.

The lure of a lollipop ensured that quite young boys would fetch and carry bales of gloves; Emma kept a large sweet jar in her window to encourage their eagerness.

The drainage workers returned home to a tremendous welcome. They looked lean, tired and hungry; but in their eyes financially well off. They were bombarded with questions. They proudly handed over all the money they had earned to their mothers. No son handled his own finances until he was twenty-one years old. Mothers expected this when each son was born. This kept each family as a unit, each member helping to keep his team together. This situation was envied by those families who, years before, had produced more female offspring than male.

Those lads who had remained in the village and were now approaching seventeen were envious and enthusiastically appealed to John for the future, but he made no promises or refusals. John offered the boys no hope for the future, he just confirmed that the next four winter months would be spent at home.

This homecoming guaranteed that all these young lads would be attending 'The Prims' this winter. The community was viewing this journey into the unknown as a pioneering adventure.

John on the other hand had imminent jobs that needed his attention. A calf, born in the spring, had been carefully nurtured by Emma and was now ready for market. The sow would soon farrow. The fatted pig was ready to be killed. The thought of home cured ham and bacon excited him, as did the liver and brawn and chitterlings. Nothing could compare with the taste and smell of that pure white lard, sprinkled with salt and crackling rosemary.

Yes, he was secretly anticipating a few months of home cooking. Fizzy pop and apple pies with lashings of cream; the expectation was nearly too much to bear. He needed to replace both his body weight and stamina.

His benefactor was due to arrive in a few days and he would walk to Witney to meet him. These meetings were now less frequent, but, for different reasons, they each anticipated them with secret understanding. Leo was as generous as always; after the usual meal, a trip to the tailor and cordwainer. Leo would enquire after the wellbeing of John's mother, but

The machine at Newlands, now powered by electricity.

a meeting was never suggested. There was a 'man to man' handshake as they parted, but no fatherly love ever existed – although Leo always viewed John with inward pride.

In a curious way John was relieved when the parting was over. He would anchor his roots in Freeland again, his mind was buzzing with the idea of another working backpack. His idea of pleasure was to accompany those lads again, bringing them safely home after months of toil and sweat, knowing he had benefited all.

But his father was now an old man. Since John's illness Leo had realised that this was a son who could never inherit, despite his early aspirations in that direction. Shortly before the first world war John mysteriously received what was for that time the very substantial sum of one thousand pounds. We can only presume that this came from Leo's will. He had no use for the money himself, and put it in government bonds where it remained in the family until 1990.

John's home and garden was now classified as a 'smallholding' but his role was to supervise while the females were employed physically. He would plant a small plot with corn, he would erect netting to enclose the hens, he would walk to Pinsley Wood to get bundles of pea sticks, but the hard graft of cleaning out the pigs, milking the cow and even digging was the predestined fate of the women.

When John was at home, money was never restricted. He ordered all the household's needs. A sack of flour was purchased for Kesiah to make bread. The list included a sack of dried peas, his usual crates of fizzy pop and anything else that attracted him.

When he was away there was so much food left grown by the women – including bacon and ham and potatoes, milk and eggs – that very little money was needed, just enough to allocate to the weekly collection plate at the chapel.

The females were occupied every second of every day, indeed if ever a 'time and motion' study was needed, it was here. They had no real leisure or pleasure, but they did look forward to any caller who needed half a dozen eggs or any child who could afford a lollipop.

While so much work was being done by so few hands, the housework was becoming more and more neglected.

# — 17 —

# John's life is mapped out

John was twenty-four years old when he returned from Great Amwell with the Freeland lads. He felt an inward pride that he had initiated such an adventure with such pioneering experiences, and that it had proved so successful. The boys now had such positive confidence in themselves, they were ready to tackle anything.

John knew he was having a great effect on young lads, more than their uneducated fathers could even imagine. He said little, but each word he spoke was heeded, each word he spoke was a lesson. He was dreaming of the day when he would accompany mature lads; he would show them how to use a bank and write a cheque. Who had ever heard of a poor man having a bank account?

He knew that he would be going again next year but he calculated that it was not advisable to raise enthusiasm too much in his fellow travellers. There could be hazards; inclement weather or illnesses could strike at any time.

John was finding his direction in life, now that he had spent so many hours in their chapel, both listening and adhering to the teaching. The services combined prayer, praise and preaching, but to this branch of Methodism, preaching was considered to be the most important.

A large majority of the congregation had no formal education so it was at chapel that they learnt right from wrong, morals, and manners. They were taught that each had talents and individually they must seek out those talents, then act positively using them to their utmost abilities. John felt that he was acting on this teaching. He also felt that this type of adventurous spirit was infectious, the individuals, the families, and the whole community would benefit.

John had no interest whatever in marriage. He had seen too much of a high birth rate coexisting with a high death rate. He had seen too many women dying in childbirth. He had seen too many small children dying of measles or whooping cough. Lack of medicine, knowledge, bad housing, and very little money all contributed to this situation which we think was frightful and horrific. They learnt to live, cope and accept their lot and appreciate any small streak of luck that came their way.

We know that John went to Great Amwell again the following year. A few extra lads joined them and the adventure was equally successful. This was in 1882 and although John continued his travels there doesn't appear to be any knowledge of his destinations until 1896 when my two uncles were old enough to join the ever-increasing numbers. These two uncles were, of course, John's nephews.

We do know that during those intervening years he did stay at home for at least one summer. During that summer he supervised the building of his 'dairy'. It was a cold room added to the cottage to contain the milk pans, butter churn etc. and it was also very useful for his fizzy pop. The floor was dug out to about two feet lower than the house to ensure an equable temperature for milk, butter and eggs. It served its purpose very well, but being built with red bricks onto a stone cottage ensured its demolition and a short life.

John was now communicating with hopeful employers securing more work, and this year, 1896, he was directed towards Worcester. The Great Western Railway needed branch lines, which entailed much digging.

He viewed those fruitful expeditions as his predetermined destiny. It was based on, and encouraged by, the teaching he had received in the chapel and from 'The Good Book'. He looked upon this as his calling and mission in life – it was a public service of which he was justly proud.

The same hymns that they sang so lustily in the Freeland chapel, they sang again on their travels.

By now John's team of diggers numbered more than forty. They met as usual at the Freeland chapel but they represented many villages and towns like Woodstock or Witney. They enjoyed the trip to Worcester, which had the same happy ending.

More and more praise was heaped on John but he was oblivious to it, he always controlled the finances but he shared the profits fairly. He was calculating the best offers now, developing into a modern union man. He did of course hold a monopoly, he was secretary, treasurer and sole administrator. He was in fact a committee of one, but it worked well, firstly because he was better educated but also because he was aloof which meant there was never any favouritism. He had time to think, indeed that was all he seemed to do. This situation ensured that everyone thought that he was winning.

The following year found them back in the fens in a hamlet called Pode Hole, much nearer to Spalding. The rate of pay had improved, and the area of suggested drainage had multiplied. Everyone was delighted; excitement built up as they walked home. Why do we walk a hundred miles each way for just one summer? Could we not overstay one winter?

They were keen, John knew the families were keen, so he reasoned, why should he stand in their way, why should I discourage such fervour and enthusiasm?

This was the first time John had listened; this time he thought it was sound advice so they decided to over winter in Spalding.

The first pumping station built at Pode Hole in the 1880s.

— 18 —

# The going gets tough

So in the early spring of 1898 an excited and eager body of youths, resembling the children of Israel ready to leave Egypt, met at the Freeland Chapel. The whole village was there to wish them well.

The journey was long and strenuous but never boring. John, as always, led the way. Now, at the age of forty, he was still keen. He still left his mother at home to supervise both the stock and the garden. He had not seen his benefactor for more than a year.

His younger half-sister Kesiah was still there but she was beginning to think that life was passing her by; she did not approve of the youth of the village being displaced for one year, and this time it was two years. She had much work piled on her and she did not object. Her attendance at chapel was less enthusiastic and less optimistic than before. The congregation consisted of married couples with their families or those much too old or too young.

There must have been many girls with identical worries. This annual trek had been taking place for nearly twenty years and the number of spinsters was increasing. John would not have thought of this, because to him it was an insignificant detail. He would never have thought of it as a problem.

They reached their destination after several days with no serious worries. The fields were flat and waterlogged and many groups had already arrived.

They all enjoyed the work, a good communal spirit existed between them. The ultimate outcome would be a life not distorted by struggling to make ends meet or by starvation. The winter months were not good; they worked through rain and floods but frost brought insurmountable problems.

John helped them to write letters home, they each did their utmost,

Digging out the new channel for the River Welland, improving drainage by enabling the river to reach the sea more quickly.

**Above**: a steam dredger at work.
**Below**: horsepower pulls a barrow up the ramp on the River Nene at Wisbech.

then for reasons of economy the letters were tied into one small parcel and sent to the chapel.

John did no physical work but his time was well occupied. He was the intermediary between the bosses and the labourers. He organised the tools and listened to the grievances, which were now multiplying due to the conditions under which they worked. He took charge of the menu; he was sometimes called on as a doctor when illnesses occurred.

He was not happy now, he felt that he needed a few months to recuperate. The boys did not admit it, but he was sure they felt the same. The winter was long and severe and boredom set in. They must stick it out because they alone had suggested it. John was also taking some of the blame as he had allowed it.

When spring arrived they were anxious to work every possible day, but the spirit was not the same and there was less pride in their work. Some had not survived the winter too well, some took days off, some tried to work when they were clearly unfit.

The more the sun shone the better they worked. The health of some was causing concern. John was perfectly well, he coaxed if needed but it

Manning the sluice.

was also his lot to order them to bed on several occasions.

Every day brought more worry for John. He did not mention the terrible word that was raising its ugly head. There was far too much coughing amongst the lads. One of his nephews was suffering badly, so in mid-August John decided that enough was enough, they cut short their stay and headed towards home.

They were somewhat deflated, the spring in their step had gone. John was dedicated to getting them home before the situation worsened. They all were obliged to travel at the speed of the weakest. When only about five miles from home, George, John's youngest nephew, collapsed.

John's initiative was called on again. He trudged to the nearest farm begging a large, strong corn sack which, after cutting holes in each corner, he converted into a stretcher with ash poles from the hedge.

John organised a rota, committing all those who were still able. Working in teams of four they carried George shoulder high on this home-made stretcher. It worked, progress was a little faster now.

So it was that now, about two miles from Woodstock, they heard the discordant notes of the local band. To them it was encouraging, they were nearly home and yes, they were all still alive. No matter if some of the notes were less than perfect, to them the music was beautiful.

They arrived at Georgina's in a mixed state of strain, despondency yet happiness. The tired lads all dispersed to their separate villages. John, after a good meal, headed back to Freeland. He would rest in his own chair, see his own mother and sister and receive some homely comforts. The worry connected with the health of the lads was now transferred to the parents.

What had happened to little Jackie, Georgina's youngest son? She just said he had gone to heaven. That dreaded word was not spoken aloud, but John knew and understood.

Yet another shock was awaiting him. While he was away, Kesiah had been tempted; life was passing her by, so she had yielded. A new born baby daughter had arrived.

What would happen now? Would she have to leave home? Could John adjust to such a new comer?

# 19

# What a winter!

John had walked in very tired, near to exhaustion, worried about the health of several lads and at least contemplating some needed rest to both body and mind. He was thunderstruck, this staggering situation had rendered him speechless. Such an event had never been envisaged. He knew little about babies, but enough; he did not expect or want to learn any more.

The cottage was small, just two bedrooms, and a small landing. One room for Emma, their mother, one for John which contained a very long bed made to John's measurements. Kesiah always slept on the landing but the space was not adequate to cope with a full-size bed and a baby.

In John's absence Kesiah had moved into his room but now that must change. While the baby was small Kesiah could manage on the old chesterfield in the living room and the baby could sleep on in the empty drawer.

John lay back in his own bed that night, but sleep eluded him. He was the man of the house and he must seek out a solution to the problem.

A brainwave manifested itself the following day. John had a very long garden but at the end of it a farm cottage, just visible, was standing unoccupied. He would find the owner and buy it. So, without discussion with any other family member, he met the owner in the pub, paid for the house with cash and returned home with the deeds. He handed the document to Kesiah.

'This property is yours,' he said.

Kesiah showed no sign of emotion as she accepted the present, she would have to grow in confidence overnight. She now had a baby to mother and an empty house, without even a saucepan. Her only income came from her gloving. She would still help in the garden so eggs, vegetables and fruit would still be available.

John did not neglect his sister, nor ignore the obligations which he considered were his own. He called daily at the cottage to help finance any necessities.

He also visited the lads who had manfully urged and coaxed each other home under extreme circumstances.

The winter brought the worst possible weather. The awful illness crawled painfully from house to house, village to village, seeking out any weak host who would knuckle under. John's two nephews followed each other to the churchyard. Their mother, Georgina, drained by too many births, gave up the struggle at the end of January, simultaneously with the Queen who plunged the whole nation into mourning.

There never had been a winter like this. The scourge did not respect class or wealth; it appeared to survey each habitation, then attack even the youngest, strongest male. By the onset of spring nearly every family had been affected, some very badly.

During this winter Georgina's widower, George, had been building his house in Long Hanborough. It was designed to house a large family, now so depleted since the family was in need of a mother. The following year George married Clara Long, who moved into the new house.

Only four girls were left now, the eldest being Queenie who was nearly blind. She made no effort to welcome or understand the addition of a stepmother to the family. Queenie regarded her as an usurper, but this feeling was mutual, Clara clearly wanted her gone.

Queenie, although handicapped, was no handicap to a family, she was actually an asset and a blessing. She appealed to her Uncle John and was offered the landing, so recently vacated by Kesiah.

# 20

# The unconventional family

Queenie had a nondescript, mundane job at the local paper mill. Although she was living much nearer to the mill now she was given the choice to keep or leave the employment. She chose to leave.

Many of Kesiah's responsibilities would now fall on Queenie. She could turn the churn handle to make the butter, she could run all the errands, and she was extremely expert at sewing. Housework was impossible and she was never allowed to do gloving as the factory treated them very severely if a glove was accidentally soiled. Cooking was beyond her, the heat from an open grate was too dangerous.

I remember watching her scrubbing a white deal-topped table. Her head, down at table level, was tilted at an angle resembling the little dog of His Master's Voice fame. Gripping the brush with two hands and using unlimited elbow grease, she worked with determination and vigour. She would wring the cloth tightly and wipe away all excess of soapy water. She gave extra attention to the edges of the table; any job undertaken by Queenie was done thoroughly. She was so proud of her effort that no one attempted to enlighten her as to the blobs of soapy bubbles that were lying equidistant on the floor beneath the edges of the table.

She busied herself during the week delivering telegrams and spreading every scrap of news she heard. She spent her Sundays attending either chapel or church, whichever door happened to be open. She never missed a christening, wedding or funeral.

Every bit of tittle-tattle she could collect, she broadcast far and wide. She had a very noticeable habit of talking to herself.

The death of Georgina and all her sons had been traumatic, almost too much for Emma to bear. It was more than flesh and blood could stand. She outlived her daughter by only two years and to the end she was always convinced that it was the arrival of John some forty years earlier that had saved them from starvation.

John disguised his feelings as always but they were there all right. He was still accepting some of the blame, while at the same time the nation mourned its queen.

He was now left in the cottage with only his niece, Queenie, whose willpower was resolute but whose ability was fraught with dangers. There was not sufficient sleeping space to accommodate both Kesiah and her daughter. By mutual consent she would return to the cottage everyday, just using her own cottage for them to sleep in.

As the undertakings of the stock and garden became too much for the mixed bunch of humans, slowly the duties were dispensed with. The cow had gone, then the pigs, but the hens scratched around at their will, sometimes where they should be, but mainly where they should not.

John paid all the family bills and Kesiah coped with most of the work. John's huge body made digging very difficult. Any garden tool that was bought for him could not be used until it had a longer handle. This worked well with hoe or rake and he was very willing to do that work. Digging was much more difficult. It was nearly impossible to balance the fork and push it into the ground with that huge boot. He needed a fork with a much broader shoulder. With the longer handle Kesiah was unable to use it, and as for John, when he levered the fork, the fulcrum was too high making the spit of soil too heavy. So now as before the heaviest digging was undertaken by Kesiah while John carried on hoeing with his very long-handled hoe.

This mode of survival continued until Kesiah's daughter was thirteen, when she was ushered into service and Kesiah returned to John's cottage.

John now, as always, was living only with females; he could barely remember his grandfather from the dim and distant past.

Why he undertook to help so many lads can only be imagined.

Did he want to cut himself off from girls and women?

Was he trying to live his life exactly as he had been taught at chapel?

Was it because he loved walking and taking control of each situation?

We only know it was his choice alone.

# 21

# From horse to hen

In the same month that Kesiah's daughter Ida left this world, I decided to make my entrance. This was July 1920.

We come now to John's declining years, which I remember very well.

John had never lived with any male since his grandfather died when he was small. He had never attempted any housework; he expected a lot from his womenfolk. It is difficult to imagine him doing housework, remembering that standing up straight was a problem, similarly getting down low. His feet were a definite handicap. An outside life was really his only choice, at least he could walk upright.

He now had a few friends who shared his outdoor life. They all supported Freeland's cricket and football teams. John had their new cricket bats made at Combe mill. They walked to all the local villages; genuine loyal supporters. Although they took no part in the local garden shows, they always went to view the produce of others. And they enjoyed the village brass band, which was now very popular.

When we were small children, we often went to John's house as a family, which was a walk of about five miles. It was the only way to get there and we did not think it was a hardship.

I always thought of them as rich relations. Perhaps I was comparing their standard of living with our own. My father, in farming, was striving to keep afloat. He couldn't sell his crops, he lost several horses, he had three small children. Farming has always been a lottery.

When we went to Freeland, we looked forward to food that we never otherwise saw. That lovely pop that John himself controlled was a big attraction. It was freely handed out. There was always a large bag of cream cakes, it included cream horns, eclairs and cream slices. We could only dream of such delicious feasting. At home we had to be content with homemade lardy cakes.

The author, aged about 13, picking apples at the Freeland cottage. Queenie is anchoring the ladder.

They had a large two-tier safe that was kept in the dairy. It was used to keep food away from flies and the dairy was the coolest place they had. In it was always a large oval dish with a cooked joint, usually ham or beef. Slices were cut at will. I imagined that was how rich people lived while we were thankful to survive on humble rabbit stew.

Kesiah's daily routine was demanding drudgery. Getting in fuel, taking up the ashes and lighting the fire were the chores she did before the others came down. They always had a coal fire, even in the summer;

it was their only means of cooking. She also cleaned and filled the oil lamps.

During the morning Kesiah always made pastry. She had a large pie dish, which used to be white enamel but heat and age had changed it to a dirty yellow. That pie – apple, rhubarb, or plum – was always cut into four equal parts. That was one each for midday meal and one left for John just before going to bed. They had lashings of cream daily. I still have Kesiah's rolling pin and have used it all my married life.

Washing facilities for both humans and clothes were at a minimum. There was no copper but they had a huge cast iron pot that would only just balance on the hob. Too dangerous, I thought, but I did once see John's shirt bubbling away in it. It was too heavy to move, so the water was ladled in and out with a hand bowl. Most of the washing was rubbed with soap, and in spite of her poor eyesight, it was done by Queenie. To put it mildly, clothes were only washed when they really needed it.

Each year that passed saw the women putting on more and more weight. John's physique did not alter.

Both the women wore many gathered petticoats and an apron was tied tightly over all. It was tied so tightly making a bulge both above and below the waist. These bulges attracted dirt; one round patch below the waist and two crescent shaped ones above. Their sleeves were usually rolled up, proving to the world that they were doing the work.

Their lavatory was a very long way down the garden, adjoining a shed that was used for straw and hay. It had twin 'holes' just in case circumstances demanded their use. They did have a commode, but if they used it… poor Kesiah!

The staircase was twisty and steep and turned over the fireplace as it ascended.

John spent virtually all the daylight hours outside. While he was out the hens took over. Queenie tried in vain to keep them out. She could only hear them so her efforts were futile. Kesiah did her best too; she followed them around the house and garden seeking out their nests. They had become so friendly they could often be seen perching on the settee or even on the table. This was a room that three people lived in. Queenie couldn't see it needed cleaning, John couldn't care and Kesiah was too overworked to bother and considered it was useless to try.

So it was in October 1940, at the age of eighty-three, midst Rhode

Island Reds and Light Sussex, after a very short illness, John suffered a fatal heart attack, brought on by senility (so the death certificate records).

The undertaker arrived and put a trestle table in the coal house. John lay there surrounded by coal and hens till he was carried to the church-yard.

So John, who had come into the world in a stable, left it in a hen house.

For a list of other local history books published by
The Wychwood Press, please phone 0845 458 3460, or write to
The Wychwood Press,
Alder House, Market Street,
Charlbury OX7 3PH

Please email wychwood@joncarpenter.co.uk to be informed of
new titles as published